July	August	September	October	November	December	
						Mon
	1					Tues
	2					Wed
	3					Thu
	4				1	Fri
1	5			4	2	Sat
2	6	3	1	5	3	Sun
3	7	4	2	6	4	Mon
4	8	5	3	7	5	Tues
5	9	6	4	8	6	Wed
6	10	7	5	9	7	Thu
7	11	8	6	10	8	Fri
8	12	9	7	11	9	Sat
9	13	10	8	12	10	Sun
10	14	11	9	13	11	Mon
11	15	12	10	14	12	Tues
12	16	13	11	15	13	Wed
13	17	14	12	16	14	Thu
14	18	15	13	17	15	Fri
15	19	16	14	18	16	Sat
16	20	17	15	19	17	Sun
17	21	18	16	20	18	Mon
18	22	19	17	21	19	Tues
19	23	20	18	22	20	Wed
20	24	21	19	23	21	Thu
21	25	22	20	24	22	Fri
22	26	23	21	25	23	Sat
23	27	24	22	26	24	Sun
24	28	25	23	27	25	Mon
25	29	26	24	28	26	Tues
26	30	27	25	29	27	Wed
27	31	28	26	30	28	Thu
28		29	27		29	Fri
29		30	28		30	Sat
30			29		31	Sun
31			30			Mon
			31			Tues

Grune	August	Spune	Sektober	Ember	December

DISCWORLD
Assassins' Guild
Yearbook and Diary
2000

PERSONAL DETAILS

Name _____

Degrees _____

Prizes _____

Name of House _____

Name of House Master _____

Name of Crocodile _____

Family Motto (if applicable) _____

_____

Species _____

Gender (if known) _____

Vital Status   Living/Dead/Undead/Other

Date of Birth/Death _____

Next of Kin (to be contacted in case of inhumation)

_____

Home Address _____

_____

_____

_____

_____

Religion/Cult _____

Favourite Weapon _____

Favourite Concealed Weapon _____

Favourite Old Boy _____

Favourite Impression of Mr Lamister _____

_____

Hobbies _____

Favourite Client _____

Most Challenging Commission _____

_____

Amount of Orno _____

Lord Downey, Head Master

I would like to take this opportunity to welcome to the Guild of Assassins (Conlegium Sicariorum) those boys, and especially those girls, who have joined the Guild this Term.

'CS', as you will hear the Guild referred to by Masters and pupils, has a long and, on occasion, proud history. Our Old Boys have gone on to make their mark in politics, religion, and all branches of government. Admittedly, in many cases, those marks have been difficult to see with the naked eye, because we pride ourselves on not being unnecessarily messy.

Many Old Sicarians now hold offices of great power and authority on the Disc: King Pteppicymon XXXXX of Djelibeybi and our own, much loved, Lord Vetinari (currently the Provost of the Conlegium), to name but two.

Here at the Guild we pride ourselves on educating the *whole* person (experiments in educating small parts of them having failed in the past) on all aspects of social life and, of course, death. As well as the subjects of direct relevance to the Guild's foundation, we also provide a thorough grounding, which is second to none, in subjects as diverse as Languages, Drawing, Quartering – just my little joke – Geography, Dance & Drama, Alchemy, Embroidery, Advanced Weaponry, History, Brewing and all manner of out-door sports. I myself take sixth-formers for advanced classes in poisoning, and I can assure you that my wife's Thursday afternoon teas, which they are expected to attend, are an education in themselves.

An Old Sicarian can hold up his or her head – or in some cases on unusual assign-ments *someone else's* head – in polite society, secure in the knowledge that he (or she) has been trained to deal with any situation that may arise, particularly if it involves edged weapons.

And thereby hangs a great misunderstanding. People seem to believe that the Assassins' Guild school trains its pupils to kill people. I cannot imagine how they got that idea. Of course, many alumni do go on to join that most select branch of the diplo-matic profession, but increasing numbers of you are, I know, joining as Oppidans, quite correctly seeking to benefit from our superb education without intending eventual 'field' membership of the Guild. In this we are moving with the times.

Some of you, I dare to hope, will find our curriculum bringing out from within you certain . . . *talents* which a life in the Guild will allow you to develop to the full. But *all* of you, as you make your way in the world and possibly attract the envy of others who may therefore employ the Guild against you, may well have cause to bless the day that you paid attention in the classes on Defence Techniques.

Nevertheless, the Assassin is no murderer. A trained Assassin has honour, flair, panache, a certain *je ne sais quoi*. Above all, an Assassin has Rules. No mere muggers in dark alleyways we. Ahem, . . . let me rephrase that . . . we are not mere muggers in dark alleyways, or exponents of the long-range crossbow. We do not shoot people down in the street. We inhume with style, elegance and care. The client – and we take the view that it is the recipient of the service who should be termed 'the client' – will always be given a chance, if they are alert or provident or observant enough, to escape, evade or even defeat the Assassin. Anything else is mere butchery. Worse than that, anything else is bad manners.

And may I say that should you in later life find your path is crossed by a member of the Guild, you will have the warm, if brief, satisfaction of knowing that you have been inhumed by a fellow Sicarian who has learned tact, skill and the arts of painlessness.

I would like to take this opportunity to welcome a few newcomers. Firstly, I'm sure that many of you have already heard of Miss Alice Band, who comes to us fresh from her recent expedition to the lost Spider Temple of Fafaree, where she succeeded not only in getting all three parts of the Golden Sword of the Spider God, but also rendered no fewer than five endangered species completely extinct! There is a lesson there for all of us!

A welcome too to our new sports master, Mr Ifor Bradlofrudd, from Llamedos, who will be taking over responsibility for Sport and Hand-to-Hand Combat and will, I understand, be introducing a tribal game which neatly combines both.

Let me also extend the hand of friendship to the scholarship boys. The Guild has always regretted that accidents of birth or wealth close the door on a Guild career to many young people, and so there are a number of Guild and individual scholarships every year. Four new boys, survivors of the rather boisterous competitive entrance examination, will be joining up this year in Welcome Soap House and will be allowed to mix with the fee-paying pupils in carefully controlled circumstances.

We also welcome Jasper 'James' Chrysoprase, nephew of Mr Chrysoprase the well-respected businesstroll, who comes from excellent strata. I am sure he will do famously.

But, of course, the most exciting news this year is that we are opening our doors to the fairer, I dare not say *weaker* sex, ahaha, for the first time. The first light of the Century of the Anchovy will find us a fully co-educational establishment (within reasonable limits, of course). No longer will the sisters of our pupils have to languish at home, forced to practise their skills with girlish inexpertise on the domestic staff, hah hah. Of course, we know now that some were not content to remain so and enrolled anyway, relying on a short haircut and a forged note from their parents about doing sport. Mme les Deux-Épées herself (now the House Tutor of the new all-girl BlackWidow House, formerly Tarantula House) famously became Captain of Fencing here without causing comment beyond the fact that 'he' was rather shy in the showers.

I am quite sure that before too long the girls of BlackWidow and the proposed Mantis House will be showing us all that the female of the species *is* deadlier than the male and, of course, rather more attractive.

In conclusion, I would like to assure you that the staff of CS are here to help you. If you are in distress please speak to your Prefects who will, if necessary, refer you to your Tutor, to the Scullion or to me. My door is always open. Well, my window is always open – doors are too easy for students at Old Sicarius, haha.

Remember our watchword – It is a Noble Thing to Lay Down Someone Else's Life for Your Country. And, of course, to get a receipt.

Conlegium Sicariorum

Memorandum

TO ALL STAFF

From the Head Master

I must tell you all that, following the experiment last term, the Guild Council has voted to accept young ladies on the roll this year. I am aware that a number of you have strong feelings on this issue, but there you are. We must be seen to move with the times.

We are also taking on our first troll. Again, I am aware of the arguments. However, the Chrysoprase family is paying for the new Alchemy laboratory and I have met the young troll in question. He has an exuberant tendency to violence that only needs harnessing to practical purposes for him to become a valuable member of the Guild.

Incidentally, I have noticed a growing tendency for boys to go around the City without their hands in their pockets, and in some cases even to progress with a firm, upright step. Assassins – even in training – do *not* march. They move with a languid, even *louche* step, and tend to lean against things and yawn in a knowing way. Any boy found sitting up straight is to be sent to my study immediately. To be a pupil here is to be a lord of creation. People expect an Assassin to have a certain style, after all. Without style, we are rather expensive thugs.

I am sure you will all be pleased to learn that no less than AM$1,100 was raised for a memorial plaque to Mr Stanley 'Touché' Danpipe (Fencing) whose clean death at the end of last term at the hands of P. Phelps, Lower Fifth, was a lesson to us all in both style and duty. It will be engraved with his last words, which were 'Very good, boy. A marked improvement since last year. Aaargh.'

Downey

O n arrival at the Guild, you will be greeted by your House Master, who will appoint an older boy to act as your guide for your first few days at CS. The following are brief descriptions of the main areas of the Guild that you'll need to be familiar with in your early days.

A brief stroll around the Main Quad

Do not neglect the Porter's Lodge, wherein may be found Stippler the porter. His father was porter here, as was *his* father. He has seen it all, and the few bits he hasn't seen he can guess at. Do not attempt to play japes on him. He will remember your face, and you will find your time here clouded by all the many ways a school porter can make a boy's life a subtle misery. Tip him a shilling and the world will be a happier place.

Your path will then lead out into the quadrangle, dominated by its statue of Ellis William Netley, the student who, when playing the Wall Game, first picked up the ball and hurled it with such force that he knocked an opposing player off a second-storey window ledge. He was beaten senseless for this, but his action changed the Game from the rather insipid ball game that it was to the thrilling and bloody spectacle it is today.

To one side of the quad you can still see the new masonry of the repair to the museum wall after the unfortunate events concerning the removal from office of the previous Master, Dr Cruces. You will learn more about this early in your stay here. Let us just say for now that he was tempted to disobey one of the major rules of the Guild.

Looking up, you can see the bell tower, topped by the Guild's famous cloaked man weathervane (known as 'Wiggy Charlie'), which has oft been decked with porcelain chamberpots and female undergarments by waggish students on Wag Days.

Returning to the cloister, we turn and walk along, past the oil paintings and busts of famous inhumees. The first bust, of a former Crown Prince of Brindisi, is now almost unrecognizable as generations of student Assassins have patted his regal nose for luck. His plaque records that he 'Departed this vale of tears on 3 Grune, Year of the Sideways Leech, with the assistance of the Hon. K. W. Dobson (Viper House)'.

We now turn into the Combination Corridor, leading past the Museum. The Museum is very instructive; time spent in sober reflection there is never wasted. One exhibit which usually exercises the minds of boys for many a long night is the one-armed teddy bear (Mr Wuggle) used by Croydon Minimus to inhume the Baron von Wendeltreppe-Steckenpferd in 1687. Since that fateful day, the Wendeltreppe-Steckenpferds have never allowed any soft toys within twenty miles of their castle in Uberwald.

Beyond the Museum, we reach Big School, which used to be the Guild's only classroom. It now serves principally as the Banqueting Hall and is also used for indoor sports, assemblies and examinations. Big School is the oldest unaltered room in College and its beams, despite their inaccessibility, have been carved with the names of most of the Guild's most famous Old Boys.

Just before the multi-denominational Chapel, there is a small door leading up to the bell tower, which houses the Inhumation Bell. This tolls the hours but, as befits the City's principal academy, it is always fashionably late. It also is tolled whenever news comes through of an Assassin successfully completing an assignment or upon the death of an old pupil of the college. Of course, this may quite often be one and the same event.

Proceeding further round we come to Liming Corridor which leads past Mr Wilkinson's Study to the Library. This is believed to be the largest Ankh-Morpork library outside Unseen University and, in the areas of assassination and other life-threatening professions, we like to think that it exceeds even UU's holdings of relevant tomes.

The Guild extends to five floors, excluding basements, dormer levels and lofts. The best way to explore the rest is as opportunities permit! Much of the building is out of bounds but, as Lord Downey would say, 'No one became a great Assassin by always obeying the rules. Of course, no one ever became a great Assassin by disobeying the rules *and getting caught*, either.'

At some time in their career, every pupil will see the inside of the Master of Assassins' study. Some will go for a cup of tea, a chat and the automatic avoidance of an almond slice, some will be going for a punishment, some will have been sent up for good, some will be going to receive bad news. In most cases they will not therefore be in a frame of mind to take in the details, but these are worth noting as the room is a classic example of a Guild study.

Impressive, oak-panelled and well-carpeted, it also serves as the Guild Council Chamber. Indeed, to one side you will see the Council's long, mahogany table. The room also contains the Master's own library and workbench – and who knows what mysterious substances may be stored in the dozens of intriguing drawers in his apothecary cabinet?

The study is dominated by the four huge black granite pillars that support the ornate ceiling. Four-square between those pillars, carved as they are with the names of famous Assassins, is the Master's desk, with its wrought-iron rack for birches and canes. These are a relic of the old days. In the modern college, we do not believe in anything so namby-pamby as corporal punishment.

A History of the Guild

Classically, assassination as a profession began in the more mountainous regions of Klatch, where aspirants would partake of a drug known as *hasheesh* which, in sufficient quantities, would cause them to wear flared trousers and listen to really monotonous music with every sign of enjoyment.

Those early 'assassins' then disappeared into history and emerged somewhat later in the form we now recognize them. Possibly their source of supply dried up.

The Guild as it exists today owes a great debt to its founders, Sir Gyles and Lady de Murforte. Sir Gyles was a warrior knight in the days of King Cirone I (Cirone the Unsteady). He quested extensively in Klatch for the greater glory of gold and, during one of his longer crusades against any Klatchians who had money, he learned of the brotherhood of assassins. At this time they were practising their craft for general hire and were already playing an important role in the internal politics of the Komplezianne Empire, rulers of Klatch at that time.* He was so impressed by the skill, poise, intelligence and wit of those Klatchian assassins whom he met (socially) that, far-sighted man that he was, he vowed to form a school for assassins in his native Ankh-Morpork. It was recorded by his clerk that his actual words were 'Onne daye we will neede to beat thys barstads atte theyre owne game.'

On his return to the city, he talked of his plans with his wife Lady de Murforte. She wholeheartedly supported her husband and he altered his will to leave most of his lands on the Sto Plains and many valuable sites in Ankh-Morpork for its construction.

Work on the new school began in 1511. Tutors were brought in from Klatch to train the city's brighter academics and psychopaths in the various skills needed to be a great assassin, so that the faculty should be ready when the building works had been completed. The old building on the site of the current Guild building had been a warehouse for scrolls and books and it was demolished so that a new, light, airy edifice could be erected to reflect the glory of the new school.

The de Murforte School for Gentlemen Assassins was officially opened by King Cirone II on 27 August 1512. Its first Head Master was Doctor Guillaume de Chacal. Dr de Chacal was not himself known to be an Assassin, but had been recruited direct from the prestigious Academie Quirmienne, where his reputation as a strict disciplinarian and moral leader was second to none, if one ignores a few wild accusations by people who were never able to produce any hard evidence.

The school then had 8 tutors and 72 students, known as King's Scholars. (The King had bestowed the Royal Charter on the school, together with a modest sum to fund the purchase of textbooks, weaponry and anatomical charts. The first influx of students also, as it happened, included Cirone, Prince of Llamedos, his eldest son.) All the students were then housed within the Guild building, in dormitories, or houses in the area which were then named simply after their key code on the architect's plans for the school.

Within a few years, the combination of royal patronage and the excellent standard of exam results being achieved by the now Royal de Murforte School for Gentlemen Assassins, had led to pressure from the city's wealthier inhabitants for its doors to be

---

* The byzantine and convoluted politics of that lost Empire, which ruled from the now-buried city of Komplez, in fact were responsible for our word 'complex'.

opened to students who, whilst they would benefit from the high standard of education available at the School, might not actually intend to kill people for a living. The King agreed to this extension to the School's charter and places were allocated to 24 children of citizens. These students were known as 'Oppidans', from the Latatian for 'town'.

The School went from strength to strength. Over the years, its numbers of students and staff rose, and boys were boarded in houses off-site, run by a number of women known as 'dames' because of a then-current tradition of wearing huge white drawers with red spots on and owning a dancing cow.

In 1576, the School was invited by the city's elders to elevate its status to that of a Guild, giving it voting rights in the city's Guild Council. It then changed its name to the Royal Guild of Assassins but, following the events of 1688, it wisely dropped the use of the 'Royal' from its title and restyled itself the Guild of Assassins.

Regrettably, in 1767, following a rash wager by the then head of the Guild, who believed that two pairs could beat any other hand, the freehold of the main Guild premises passed seamlessly to Sir John 'Mad Jack' Ramkin, and has remained in the possession of the Ramkin family until recently, when it became part of the marriage gift of Lady Sybil Ramkin to Sir Samuel Vimes, later His Grace the Duke of Ankh, with whom the Guild has a good working relationship.

It now has the original 72 King's Scholars (as they are still known) plus 180 Oppidans and a varying number of scholarship boys, the number of the latter usually decreasing as the term progresses. In this form it has continued to grow in reputation and influence in Ankh-Morpork and throughout the known Disc. Indeed, so great is the reputation of the Guild education that a number of students now come from Klatch.

There are many stories of Assassins meeting, in the course of business, clients who themselves were 'old boys' of the school, and singing a few verses of the old school song together before the inhumation was completed. There have been occasions where the client, shedding tears of joy at the fact that his death would be a part of the ancient and wonderful tradition, signed over a large part of his fortune to the Guild, and many Guild scholarships and bursaries are a result of this.

And of course all young Assassins know the story of Sir Bernard Selachii who, upon meeting an Assassin financed by a business rival, spent the entire evening with him, reminiscing about the great days they had shared in Wigblock House, before suggesting that they drink a toast to the old school and then, while his would-be assassin held his glass aloft, beating him to death with the brandy bottle. Subsequently Sir Bernard endowed the Sir Bernard Selachii Award for Sheer Coolth, a much coveted prize to this day.

Scholarship boy

School Prizes and Awards

Sending up for good

Despite its name, this is a good thing: it means you have produced a piece of schoolwork – practical or written – which is deemed by your tutor to be so outstanding as to merit your being sent up to the Master of Assassins' study for sherry and an almond slice. Your name is also then featured in the School Magazine. However, if you accept the almond slice, it will be in the obituary section – in CS we test, test and test again!

The Teatime Prize

This will be given after the Hogswatch and de Murforte Vacations for the two best Papers on the subject 'Who I Killed on My Holidays'. Pupils are not, of course, expected to actually *inhume* anybody, but a team of senior Assassins will assess the pupils' maps, routes, amassed information, professed target and projected methods of 'solution' before awarding the prize for the best *virtual* inhumation.

The prize is named after the late Noel Teatime, a young Assassin whose plans for the inhumation of Death, the Hogfather, the Soul Cake Duck, Old Man Trouble and several major gods were the talk of the Guild. His body has never been found.

The Blankman Divinity Prize

This is open to all boys in the Second and Third Years for the most realistic representation of the god of their choice achieved using only stale bread and sesame seeds.

Distinction in Trials

Given to the top three boys in every year at end of term Trials (exams).

The Body Trophy

Named after our popular old Under Master, Mr Wilberforce Body, this is awarded to the winning Team at the Wall Game.

The Wilkinson Cup

Awarded annually to the boy who scores most consistently high marks at Fencing.

The Pendu Illuminated Manuscript

Awarded to the boy who wins the Climbing Competition at the Sports Day. The award is simply placed atop some high building in the city, and the pupil who returns to the Guild with it is adjudged the winner. The opportunities for waylaying, trapping, ambushing and cheating make this a remarkable exercise in Assassin skills.

The Veneficus Chalice

Traditionally awarded at Gaudy Night to the pupil adjudged by the Head of Necrotic Medicine and Applied Pathology to have shown most promise in practical exercises in that specialism.

The Insidiae Plate

Presented on Founder's Day by the Provost of Assassins. The winner is the constructor of the most elaborate trap mechanism in the Show and Tell section at Open Day, although actual killing will result in disqualification.

The Ars Plumaria Cup

This is won by the pupil scoring highest marks for Personal Grooming. A much-contested award.

THE PRACTICE OF ASSASSINATION; THE RULES

(Extract from *The Noble Art*, by Lord Downey, MA)

Being aware that there must be some distinction between the Assassin and the common-murderer-for-pay which extends beyond the mere size of the payment involved, the Guild has evolved over the years a number of rules to govern the craft and prevent affairs from turning into an unseemly brawl.

In short, they are as follows:

- An Assassin will not accept a contract on anyone who is unable to defend themselves, and collateral damage to bystanders, servants, etc., is considered extremely bad form.

- Any adult who is in control of assets worth more than ten thousand dollars a year *is* considered able to defend themselves, or at least to employ someone to do it for them. It is not our fault if they do not. There is no helping some people.

- An Assassin will use only weapons that rely on his or her own strength, albeit in stored form. Thus, any kind of bow is acceptable, as is, say, a lead weight lifted and carefully placed over a door. Swords, knives, clubs, ropes and so on go without saying.

- An Assassin may also use an item that is merely moved from one place to another, as it might be a bucket of piranha fish, an electrical carpet or a chemical substance.

- An Assassin is forbidden on pain of expulsion and instant clienthood from utilizing any weapon of what we may guardedly call a *firework* nature. An Assassin uses skill and discipline, not alchemical contrivances. However, in certain circumstances compressed air has much to recommend it.

- Finally, an Assassin will only use those means which a client, if they are suitably wary and diligent, may detect and avoid. There is no honour in shooting someone from a distance in the street. The thoughtful and careful client must always have a chance. A man who cannot be bothered to test his shaving soap for poison every morning has lost the will to live.

These rules apply only within Civilization, which is defined as the Sto Plains, most of the Ramtop Kingdoms, Genua and parts of Klatch.

SURVIVING YOUR FIRST FEW WEEKS

CS has been going now for centuries and there are many expressions and names for things that exist only in the oral tradition of the school. You may find it helpful to understand some of them; failing to do so may result in small yet painful ad hoc punishments, often involving the small hairs on the back of the hand.

Snout Head Master

Big School Prep Period in the evening when students can read, work or do hobbies (not involving weaponry)

Brick Appreciative term for boy skilled in wall climbing, one of the classic Assassin skills; *also* to take part in the inter-house edificeering competitions, when a boy might 'Brick for his House'. The name, of course, refers to the fact that a skilled climber might appear to those below to be just another brick in the wall.

Bunker A boy who's spent all his 'orno' and is unable to get 'sock'

Slab A student's desk in his 'pit'

Crabs ... and **Croakers, Buzzers, Seen'emalls, Loonies, Sliders, Flat'eads, Soapies, Beddiboys, Raggies, Wiggies, Rats, Scarecrows, Tumpers, Poppies.** All semi-formal (that is to say, hallowed by time) nicknames for the various School Houses. We regret to say that the new BlackWidow House has already attracted a number of nicknames, all of them unprintable except possibly for 'Darners' (because 'they'll all end up as Seamstresses one day', according to one little lad). Ah, the inventiveness of young manhood in its prime!

Draino A boy congenitally unskilled at climbing; by derivation, any unpopular person

Edificeering, edificeer, 'to eddy' Making one's way across a building or a large part of the city without ever touching the ground. A traditional Assassin skill, now often pursued as a pure sport

* **Fagging** Acting as servant to fifth- and sixth-formers; warming beds, making toast, taking messages

Inhumer, The The Guild Magazine

Last Gasp, The Nickname for the Guild Magazine

Lists End of term assembly

> * *I think it may be time to reconsider some aspects of this, what with one thing and another. Especially the warming of beds.*

Lofting A fine Guild tradition and, to some extent, also a sport. Pupils of each House build, on the rooftops of the Guild or nearby, an eyrie or 'lofting', which may be a small shed or some more esoteric construction (the hanging 'weaver bird' lofting of Wigblock House was something of a city landmark for many years until its unfortunate collapse). They are used for initiation rites and the storage of House trophies. Typically, access is extremely difficult, and only available to a skilled edificeer. By strict tradition, no materials for lofting construction may be bought; they are generally scrounged, found, begged or stolen from the loftings of other houses.

Naturally the loftings are a target for boys from the other Houses and also from the Thieves' Guild, traditional rivals. This leads to healthy competition and a state of permanent rooftop warfare, strike and counterstrike, raid and counter-raid, which in the opinion of some senior Assassins is worth a lifetime of classroom theory. A small trophy, the Roary Pig, is awarded annually by a committee of seniors. On those occasions when it is stolen by pupils from the Thieves' Guild, no members of the lofting last in possession are allowed beer with their meals for six months.

Oppidan Originally, a pupil drawn from the population of the city. Now used for any student not studying with intent to become a full Guild member

Orno Pocket money sent from home, often entrusted to travelling bands of dwarfs

Pills Poison, and by derivation, slang for Alchemy lessons and the Alchemy Master himself

Pit Student's study

Penny Reading The annual school play (from the days when the Senior Prefect could charge a penny a head to fund the provision of entertainment for the students)

Prefect Sixth-form boys appointed by the Head Master; they keep records of boys who are late, untidy, dirty or dead, they are in charge of dormitories and can give certain punishments for infringements of the school rules. Prefects are allowed to wear the coveted badge, to use the Trumper stairway, and need not wear hats when in Town.

Prep Work assigned by the 'ushers' for completion during 'Big School Prep'

Scholar A King's Scholar, or scholarship boy. One of the students originally provided with textbooks, two quill pens, a pound of ink black, two quartos of blotting paper, a twelve-inch ruler and a six-inch dagger from the beneficence of King Cirone II. These scholars are now selected by competitive examination on the 'revised tontine' or 'last man standing' system, and their fees are paid by the Guild or by various bequests. They can be recognized by the heavy black woollen gown which they have to wear at all times, even when swimming.

Scag An untidy or unpopular boy

Scaggish Bad form, lower class

Slats School Assembly, or 'pray, say and flay' (the order usually being an interdenominational prayer, school announcement, and the flogging of serious offenders)

Slurk, slurking, slurker The classic Assassin method of movement, which may be considered as 'slinking' but with style and flair. Movement without apparent effort or undue visibility

Snoddie Cad A purveyor of snoddie from a street barrow

Snoddie Cakes, sweets, pies, &c.

Sparklers, sparkies Sixth-formers, who are traditionally allowed a certain additional flamboyance to their dress

Clamp's Tea Shop in Filigree Street. Famous for its cream buns and home-made ginger beer

Splat To fall, usually fatally, while 'edificeering', and hence any failure, disappointment, expulsion, &c.

Tallboy Member of a House edificeering society; by derivation, an all-round good chap, and the opposite of a 'draino'

Tardy-books Books maintained by the Prefects to record boys who are late for lessons or whose 'prep' is late or who are themselves terminally late

Timbralls The Guild's sports field – in a corner of Hide Park

Town Literally anywhere in the city that is not Guild property

Usher Master

TRADITIONS

The Wall Game

To the unfamilar, this appears to be a cross between urban rock-climbing, squash and actual bodily harm. It is traditionally played on the walls of the Guild's inner courtyard, but 'friendly' and practice games are played anywhere on Guild property when a wall has been adapted to mimic some of the original features (such as 'Old Mother Baggy's Washing Line', 'the Window Box', 'the Coke Heaps', 'the Wonky Drainpipe', 'the Place Where the Mortar Is Rotten' and so on). Two teams of three a side are involved, playing with a small ball made of cork wrapped in leather bands. The rules are complex, points being scored by bouncing the ball off walls and opposing players, and only one member of any team may be below 100 inches from the ground at any time. Most games run into injury time, sometimes for ever.

Pullis Corvorum

On Soul Cake Tuesday, the Guild chef catches a young magpie and attaches it to a pancake which he then nails to one of the Guild doors, incanting: 'Pullis corvorum invocantibus eum'. The poor bird is then worried to death by first-year students. A small prize, as yet unclaimed for more than two hundred years, will go to the boy who comes up with a halfway logical explanation for this.

Chapel Snoddie

The pews nearest to the high altar are occupied by the Guild's teaching staff. Immediately below them, the pews are reserved for the Prefects. Old Prefects by tradition leave small packets of almonds and raisins for their new colleagues. This is known as Chapel Snoddie. It is, of course, a ritualized test; anyone who would eat any old food found lying around wouldn't last a term.

Jasper Chrysoprase

Tumpers

It quickly became a tradition for the whole Guild to process to the Tump, where the new boys would be sprinkled with salt to instill them with wit for their coming years at CS, 'sal' meaning both salt and wit, and puns being the lowest form of the latter. Later this became a means of raising funds for Guild charities. Every year on 12 January, boys from the school go out in pairs on to the streets of Ankh-Morpork. One carries a stoneware pot of salt, the other a leather draw-string purse. They accost passers-by and encourage them to make a donation to the Guild. When they receive money, the donor is given a pinch of salt and everyone feels embarrassed.

May Blossom Day

On May Day, if the Master of Assassins gives permission and if the day is moist, the boys are permitted to rise early and collect boughs of May blossom in Hide Park and decorate with them the windows of their dormitories. The boys are, however, not allowed to get their feet wet. For the past ninety years, no boy has bothered to give it a try.

BULLYING

Bullying is not a problem at CS. We do not believe in training pupils in a protected, hot-house atmosphere. After the first few weeks all boys go armed according to their ability, and we find that in most cases a boy who is not yet skilled with the throwing knife may have a natural talent with the sword; curiously enough, the weakest and smallest boy may well be an inventive genius with poisons, and so on. After a few scuffles and the occasional inevitable fatality, we find that a careful politeness reigns amongst the surviving pupils.

The following occasions of 'acceptable horseplay' are hallowed by time and tradition:

Tossing

A New Bod and four or five heavy, leather-bound books are placed together in a large woollen blanket. Several older boys then grasp the hem of the blanket and toss the boy and books up into the air, chanting: 'Ibis ab excusso missus ad astra sago'. On 'sago', the blanket's occupant should be propelled upwards to try to hit the ceiling. Much fun can be had from the injuries caused by blows to the New Bod from the heavy books. It is considered very bad form for him to subsequently hunt down the other boys.

Toasting

This consists of cutting bread into thick slices and crudely cooking them in front of an open fire.

The term did use to have another meaning, but that custom died out, along with four boys, when, in a spirit of boyish good humour, they attempted to 'toast' a new boy, Mr Noel Teatime. The carnage that followed was an instructive example of what can be achieved with enthusiasm, determination and the common human thumb.

Ticing

When a New Bod has gone to sleep in the dorm, several larger boys enter, tie a strong rope to his big toe and then drag him out of bed, down the corridors and out into the main quad (or street, for extra-mural Houses). There the boy is stripped and tied to one of the statues (quad) or horse troughs (street). What larks.

Penning

A pen is formed by placing four beds into a square. A New Bod is placed in the pen and several larger boys then stand on the beds and kick the New Bod around the pen. Much fun can be had by betting on how long he can remain conscious before another New Bod has to be brought in to replace him. The New Bod is allowed to fight back, and should take heart from the fact that the current Head of School, Victor Ludorum, outlasted his tormentors for three hours during his first 'penning', suffocating one with a pillow, stunning another with a bedknob and strangling three others with his pyjama cord.

1 The Extremely Reverend Dr A-Pox-Upon-Their-Houses Jenkins (Religious Studies)

2 Mr Moody (Personal Grooming)

3 Baron Strifenkanen (Applied Pathology)

4 Kompt de Yoyo (Modern Languages and Music)

5 Dr von Ubersetzer (Ancient Languages)

6 M. de Balourd (Dance and Deportment)

7 Mme les Deux-Épées (Fencing and Edged Weaponry)

8 Mr Linbury-Court (History)

9 Mr Lamister

10 Lord Downey (Master of Assassins)

11 Mr Mericet (Under Master)

12 Mr Bradlofrudd (Physical Education)

13 Miss Band (Climbing, Traps, Locks)

14 Miss Smith-Rhodes (Domestic Science and Organic Poisons)

15 Professor Stone (Alchemy and Metalwork)

16 Lady T'Malia (Political Expediency)

17 Mr Graumunchen (Geography)

School Rules

1. The whole of Filigree Street and (while boating is allowed) Frost Alley and Flood Walk is in bounds. The area around the Patrician's Palace is within bounds. The direct routes between the extra-mural Houses and the Guild building are in bounds for those times when boys are travelling between one and the other. All other parts of the city are out of bounds without permission. Note: the definition of out of bounds is: 'a place where a pupil may not be seen by staff'. An Assassin will often need to spend time in places where he should not be, and this rule should supply valuable experience.
2. Boys are forbidden to enter any Theatre or Place of Public Entertainment, or Hotel, or Public House of any description, unless treating their House Tutor.
3. Boys are warned against playing card games with anyone calling themselves Doc or named after a geographical location or having a part of the body as a name, e.g., Doc Sharper, Pseudopolis Fats, Fingers McGee.
4. Boys are strictly forbidden from mentioning fruit within the hearing of the Matron.
5. Boys are warned against entering any Shops of a forbidden class, such as Tobacconists', Pawnbrokers', etc., as well as any that have been especially forbidden by the Head Master. They are also forbidden to enter any house of Ill-Repute; however, sixth-formers are allowed one (1) weekly visit to a house of Good Repute (an updated list is kept in the Porter's Lodge).
6. Boys are expressly forbidden from teasing Mr Lamister.
7. Boys are strictly forbidden to buy or to have in their possession any Spirit, Fat or Mineral Oil, or any other inflammable or explosive material, or fireworks of any description.
6. Boys are not allowed to keep ungulates of any description in their rooms.
7. No boy is to whistle in the Combination Corridor during Mr Moody's lessons.
8. Boys are not allowed to walk around the Guild or the Town without their hands in their pockets.
9. Boys may not run in the corridors of the Guild.
10. Boys may not play at Ramcat in the Big School.
11. No boy is to make Huckle-My-Buff in his room.
12. Boys are strictly forbidden to use Mr Lamister's door as a target.
13. Boys may not wear vests for Sports.
14. No boy is to wear his hair longer than shoulder length. *This rule may be relaxed if the boy is a girl.*
15. By custom and practice, boys are allowed to carve their names once upon their desks and once upon the roof leads of Big School. Boys are emphatically not allowed to carve their initials on Mr Lamister's leg.
16. No boy is to keep a crocodile in his room.
16a. No boy is to keep an alligator or any large amphibious reptile in his room.
16b. No boy, we wish to make it clear, is to keep any kind of monitor, goanna or giant chameleon in his room.
16c. Nor in the cellar.
16d. Nor in a cage on the roof.
16e. No boy is to own, rent, lease or hire any kind of lizard, amphibian or any species of creature broadly resembling the aforesaid (dead or alive) in his room, or anywhere else on, in, above or under Guild premises, or in any dimension occasionally congruent with this one, nor is any boy allowed to keep an alligator (or similar) costume, or possess a humorous inflatable alligator (or similar) that may be dangled on the end of a string in

front of the window of the study below. Pictures of crocodilians and related creatures of a size normally expected in a work of natural history are acceptable. Newts may be kept for the purposes of nature study.

16f. Boys are forbidden to keep any newt of a length greater than five (5) inches at full growth. Despite significant differences apparently visible to the educated eye, the Sumtri Fire Newt is defined as a crocodilian under School Rules, in so far as it is capable of eating a full-grown master.

16g. None of the above rules 16–16f applies to pupils who are worshippers of Offler the crocodile god.

16h. No boy is to convert to Offlerism without permission in writing from the Head Master.

16i. Any boy pretending to Offlerism may, at the whim of the Head Master, be subjected to twenty complicated questions on its tenets and beliefs. Inaccuracy in this area will result in expulsion. Religion is not a joking matter.

16j. The Guild of Assassins and its associated teaching establishment fully accept that to the worshippers of Nog-Humpy the custard god, religion *is* a joking matter.

17. Any boy found at any time (apart from in bed) not in possession of two stiletto daggers and (boys over 4′9″) a sword of suitable length, plus at least three approved concealed weapons (see list in Big School) will be expelled without appeal.

17b. Any girl found at any time (apart from in bed) without at least two stiletto daggers and three concealed weapons (see list in Matron's Office) will be expelled without appeal. Whilst aware that female clothing offers many opportunities for concealment, and whilst also aware that inventiveness should be encouraged, the following items are restricted to girls in year four and above:

    a) poisoned underthings of any description

    b) spring-loaded corsetry.

18. Girls are reminded that Miss Band's 'Porcupine' elasticated bustle bombard, whilst undoubtedly effective, has been outlawed by the Guild Council for wear anywhere within five hundred miles of Ankh-Morpork.

19. Any boy not in possession of a valid sick note who cannot, at any time, within three seconds, have a pistol bow cocked and aimed and/or a sword at the ready, will be sent to the Head Master. This applies on a 24-hour basis (apart from Swimming).

20. Boys who favour the concealed cuff bow will, pending a Guild review of the use of this weapon, refrain from wearing it at mealtimes or other occasions where it may be necessary to pass things to other pupils.

21. Poison rings are to be placed in the receptacle provided before any pupil does Domestic Science.

22. No boy shall build a deadfall in his room.

When required, for boys read girls, and vice versa.

[continued elsewhere]

Prefect

Uniform and Equipment

The correct clothing for any Assassin 'at large' is black; indeed, many Assassins wear no other colour even in their leisure hours, although deep purples and greys will not cause comment.

Boys are not allowed to wear black in their first two years, but may 'take dark' some time in their third if they are making satisfactory progress.

Boys (under 5' 6") in their first year at the Guild must wear the New Bod uniform of a midnight blue coat and knee breeches, worn with cream waistcoat and ruffled shirt, the whole capped off with a black tricorn of beaver pelt. New Bod Scholars wear white duck trousers instead of the knee breeches and, of course, their heavy woollen Scholar's gown.

Boys over 5' 6" must wear all of the above plus a sheepish expression.

First- and second-year girls of any size must wear a black gymslip or pinafore, black woollen stockings, and round hat known as the 'blonker'.

The purpose of these outfits is to make the pupils feel rather foolish, and hence determined to succeed in their studies and 'take dark' at the earliest opportunity.

After 'taking dark', pupils are expected to dress fashionably whilst eschewing bright colours; young women are enjoined not to dress in a way that might unduly inflame the amorous propensities of their male colleagues. All pupils must wear the Guild's crest on their lapel.

All pupils pursuing post-graduate studies are entitled to dress and conduct themselves as full Assassins.

NOTE. Only Prefects may carry their umbrellas furled.

Uniform and equipment on arrival at School

In addition to the list of acceptable clothing, which all parents will have received separately, the following should be found in the trunk of any new arrival:

One pair of Woollen Gloves, with cord to go through coat
One Waterproof Rain Cape
Three Sets Clothes, Black (silk and/or velvet), for Practical exercises
One Broad-Brimmed Black Hat (with cheesewire – see below)
Hairnets (girls only)
One Assassins' Guild Scarf
Five Flannelette Nightshirts (for winter terms)
One Night Cap, humorous
One pair of Slippers, preferably in pastel colours and with an animal motif (NOTE: not a
    rabbit design of any description for those boys in Cobra House or any other House to
    which Mr Lamister may be assigned)
One knitted woollen Bathing Suit
One Sports Singlet
One Sports Doublet
One Guild Dressing Gown
One Apron, floral (Domestic Science) (NOTE: Any boy or girl found with an apron decorated
    with an amusing torso or slogan such as 'Come And Get It While It's Hot' will be sent
    home.)
One Apron, leather (Alchemy)

A soft felt roll containing Throwing Knives 1, 2, 4 & 5, plus Stiletto Knives in sizes AA, AB, AC and AD

No. 3 Throwing Knife in leather thigh sheath

No. 7 Pencil Eraser

One Junior Set, Throwing Tlingas

Thin Silk Line and Folding Grappling Hook

One Chain Mail Shirt (lightweight)

One Geometry Set containing Compasses, Protractor, Divider, Set Square

One Poison Set containing phials of Wasp Agaric, Achorion Purple & Mustick

One Set, Brass Knuckles

One Soft bag of Caltraps

One Rapier and Black Velvet Baldric

One Blowpipe, 12", & Tin of Darts, Cork-Tipped with Braille identification marks

One Slingshot and Lead Ammunition (Size 12)

One Pencil Case with H, HB, B & 2B Pencils, Small Eraser (size 1) & two Pens

One Pair, Armoured Gloves

One Pair, Armour-soled Shoes (Priests)

One Set, Crampons

One Set, Pitons (various)

One Chemistry Rag

Three Karabiners

One Universal Kit – Extendable Metal Rods with Attachments, including Mirror

One 18" Ruler, marked out in tenths and in sixteenths of an inch

One Portable Inkwell (pewter)

One pair, Diamond-tipped Compasses, in pouch

One Flask of Fine Oil

One Soft Leather Roll of Lock Picks

One Apron, Canvas, for Woodworking classes

One Punch Dagger

One Junior Alchemist's Kit – with phials of Copper Sulphate, Wood Chips and Sodium Bicarbonate

Two Burleigh & Stronginthearm 'Wasp' Foldaway Pistol Crossbows and Quarrels

Two Cheesewires, suitable for concealment in brim of Hat

NOTES: It is a strict rule that *all* possessions must have a name tape sewn in, or the pupil's name die-stamped on the hilt, handle or other suitable place. This rule extends to arrows and slingshot ammunition. Cheesewires must be finished with a suitable metal label.

Some parents have queried whether or not pupils may be permitted to use blunted weapons and weapons made 'safe' by other means. Practice swords are used in initial fencing lessons. Beyond that, the Guild takes the view that 'pretend' weapons should only be used by pupils who expect to come up against artificial opponents. It is a deadly and dangerous world beyond the walls of the Guild, and it is up to us to see that it remains that way.

CONLEGIUM SICARIORUM

SCHOOL HOUSES

Viper House (Mr Nivor)
Scorpion House (Lady T'malia)
Tump House (Miss Band)
Broken Moons House (Mr Moody)
Raguineau's (Baron Strifenkanen)
Pernypopax Dampier (Professor Stone)
Cobra House (Mr Mericet)
Wigblock Prior (Kompt de Yoyo)

B2 House [day pupils](Dr von Ubersetzer)
C1 House [day pupils](Dr Perdore)
Mykkim House (Mr Linbury-Court)
Mrs Beddowe's House (M. le Balourd)
Tree Frog House [day pupils] (Mr Bradlofrudd)
BlackWidow House [girls] (Mme les Deux-Épées)
Welcome Soap House (Mr Graumunchen)
Raven House (Miss Smith-Rhodes)

GUILD OFFICERS

Provost of Assassins: Havelock, Lord Vetinari, DMAP, DM, DGS, MA, MPE, MASc, MIDD, BScI, DiPE
Master of Assassins (Head Tutor & Guild President): Lord Downey, MA
Under Master: Mr Mericet, DMAP, MA, BScI

Tutors

Political Expediency: Lady T'malia, MA, MPE, BScI
Physical Education: Mr Bradlofrudd, DiHI (Llamedos)
Fencing and Edged Weaponry: Madame les Deux-Épées, MA, DiPE
Traps and Advanced Ambush: Mr Nivor, MA, BScI
Ancient Languages: Doktor von Ubersetzer, DL
Dance and Deportment: Monsieur le Balourd, MIDD
Alchemy and Metalwork: Professor Stone, MASc
Applied Pathology: Baron Strifenkanen, DMAP
Personal Grooming: Mr Moody, BW

History: Mr Linbury-Court, MA
Modern Languages and Music: Kompt de Yoyo, DM, DL
Mathematics: Mr Schotter, MS
Geography: Mr Graumunchen, MA
Religious Studies / Chaplain: The Extremely Rev. Dr A-Pox-Upon-Their-Houses Jenkins, DGS
Climbing, Traps, Locks: Miss Band, DiPE
Domestic Science & Organic Poisons: Miss Smith-Rhodes

Guild Staff

Matron: Sister Lister, SSSHS
Bursar: Mr Winvoe, MGAU
College Porter: Mr Bracegirdle
Head Brewer (hon.): Mr Bearhugger
Chief Butler: Mr Carter, MGB

Scullion: Mr Robey
Porter: Mr Stippler
Chef: Monsieur Insignes-Fovant, FGC
Taster: (POSITION VACANT)

Student Officials

Captain of Assassins: Douglas, G.R.W.
Captain of Scholars: Bastion, C.A.T.
Captain of Oppidans: Jennings, J.C.T.
Captain of Boats: Ludorum, V.
Captain of Everything: Ludorum, V.
President of the Debating Society: Egerton, F.W.G.
Keepers of the Field: Douglas, G.R.W.; Ludorum, V.

Keepers of the Wall: Ludorum, V.; Egerton, F.W.G.
Keepers of the Weapons: Bastion, C.A.T.; Jennings, J.C.T.
Chief Chronicker: Sotley, A.
Head Dagswain: Grose, S.W.
Holder of the Humboxes: Armsbury, K.

DEGREES
(awarded both by the Guild and associated Guilds)

MA	Master Assassin	BW	Bachelor of Wig-making
MPE	Master of Political Expediency	DM	Doctor of Music
BScI	Bachelor of the Science of Inhumation	MS	Master of Sums
DiHI	Diploma of Homicidal Insanity	DGS	Doctor of Gods' Studies
DL	Doctor of Languages	SSSHS	Spiteful Sister of Seven-Handed Sek
MIDD	Member of the Institute of Dance & Deportment	MGAU	Member of the Guild of Accountants and Usurers
DiPE	Diploma of Physical Education	MGB	Member of the Guild of Butlers
MASc	Master of Alchemical Science	FGC	Fellow of the Guild of Chefs
DMAP	Doctor of Medicine & Applied Pathology			

Sumtri Fire Newt

Saturday

New Year's Day
Holiday in UK
1

Sunday

2

Octeday

FAMOUS INSTRUMENT OF DESPATCH: Grappling Hook. Mr Chidder (Viper) is believed to have successfully completed his commission by accidentally impaling the Baron von Falle with his grappling iron whilst attempting to gain entry to Schloß Blom.

3 Bank Holiday in
UK and Republic
of Ireland

Monday

4

Tuesday

5

Wednesday

6
●

Thursday

Friday

7

Saturday

8

Sunday

9

Octeday

FAMOUS OLD BOY: Johan Ludorum (Viper).
One of the greatest Assassins in the history
of the Guild. Responsible for twelve royal
inhumations. His son, Victor Ludorum
(Viper), is following in his father's footsteps
as a post-graduate and has already seen off
two Princes and a Regent during the holidays.

10   **Monday**

11   **Tuesday**

12   **Wednesday**

Tumpers

13   **Thursday**

Friday
14

Saturday
15

Sunday
16

Octeday

GUILD COMMISSION: Harold, Duke of Pseudopolis. Rather messily, with a cudgel, length of chain, pistol crossbow, dagger, poison and, ultimately, by the attachment of an anchor and immersion in water, by Prince Podgourny (not a Guild member). His Grace the Duke was a man of iron constitution and took some considerable time to be persuaded to give up. Prince Podgourny in the end had to drag the still struggling Duke to the nearby frozen river, hack a hole in the ice and then shove him in. The Prince caught a chill as a result and died three months later.

17   **Monday**

18   **Tuesday**

19   **Wednesday**

20   **Thursday**

Friday

Total eclipse
of the moon
0303–0625 hrs **21**
○

Saturday   **22**

Sunday   **23**

Octeday

School Rule No.137: No pupil is to attempt to
assassinate any other pupil during morning prayers.

24 Monday

25 Burns Night Tuesday

26 Australia Day Wednesday

27 Thursday

Friday

28

Saturday

29

Sunday

30

Octeday

OPEN COMMISSION: Rincewind (Assistant Librarian at UU) (AM$950K). Mr Rincewind is one of nature's survivors. He seems not to be a violent man, but Assassins attempting this commission seem to find themselves the victims of unexplained accidents – falling slates, lightning strikes – or, and this is worth noting, being waylaid by Mr Rincewind's travel accessory.

31 Monday

1 Tuesday

2 Wednesday
Imbolc
(Candlemas)

3 Thursday

Friday 4

Saturday 5
Partial eclipse
of the sun

●

Sunday 6
Waitangi Day
(New Zealand)

Octeday

School Rule No.139: The use of contrivances powered by springs, elastic or other means for the automated writing of 'lines' is forbidden. The writing of lines for more fortunate pupils is traditionally the province of the Scholarship Boys, who are entitled to charge one penny per hundred words.

7 Monday

8 Tuesday

9 Wednesday

10 Thursday

Friday   11

Saturday   12

Sunday   13

Octeday

MEMBER OF STAFF: Professor Stone (Alchemy and Metalwork). Professor Stone is the inventor of many of the Guild's more recent weapons, such as the tiny one-shot crossbow, concealed palm dagger and a whole range of devious jewellery. Pupils should enter his workshop with more than usual care, and be careful what they touch. Testing is not just for exams; testing is for life!

14 St Valentine's Day   **Monday**

15   **Tuesday**

16   **Wednesday**

17   **Thursday**

Friday 18

Saturday 19
○

Sunday 20

Octeday

FAMOUS INSTRUMENT OF DESPATCH: Horsehair Sofa.
Lady Prill (Viper) came up with this innovative method
to dispose of the Moon King of Brindisi. She impregnated
the horsehair with the venom of the Tezuman Tree Frog.
When the King sat on the sofa, the horsehair penetrated
the skin of his legs and he died within seconds.

21   Monday

22   Tuesday

Hobstop and Wriggle-my-Snape
may be played on this day,
in the long corridor adjoining the
Clamp. The winner is, by tradition,
awarded a cauliflower.

23   Wednesday

24   Thursday

Friday

25

Saturday

26

Sunday

27

Octeday

DISGRACED OLD BOY: Julian Fliemoe (Tree Frog). A bully and a liar, Fliemoe seemed ideally suited to his chosen profession, but he never achieved success, being an unbelievable liar and an unsuccessful bully. Mr Fliemoe was transferred to the Guild of Lawyers where these character traits worked to his advantage.

28   **Monday**

29   **Tuesday**

1 St David's Day   **Wednesday**

2   **Thursday**

Opportunity Day
Gaudy Night

Friday   3

Saturday   4

Sunday   5

Octeday

OPEN COMMISSION: Foul Ole Ron (one groat). No Assassin has been sufficiently mindless of his personal reputation to take this job. It is certainly doubtful that Mr Ron's peculiar pungency would allow any method short of an extremely accurate long-distance bowshot.

6 Labour Day
(Western Australia)
●   **Monday**

---

7   **Tuesday**

---

8   **Wednesday**

---

9   **Thursday**

Friday

10

Saturday

11

Samedi Nuite Morte

Sunday

12

Octeday

School Rule No. 145: No boy is to enter the room of any girl.

School Rule No. 146: No girl is to enter the room of any boy.

13 Commonwealth Day
Labour Day (Victoria)

Monday

14 **Tuesday**

15 **Wednesday**

16 **Thursday**

Friday

St Patrick's Day **17**

Saturday

18

Sunday

19

Octeday

School Rule No.147 (provisional): It has been pointed out that our injunction to 'read boys for girls, and vice versa', can, if taken together with the two previous rules by someone with little to do but argue, mean that no pupil is to be in any room at all. This was not the intention. No pupil is to be anywhere except where they should be. A girl is defined as a young person of the female persuasion.

20 Vernal (Spring)
Equinox

○

Monday

21

Tuesday

22

Wednesday

23

Thursday

Friday 24

Saturday 25

Sunday 26

British Summer
Time begins

Octeday

School Rule No. 148: Regardless of how persuaded he feels, Jelks Minor in Form IV is a boy.

School Rule No. 149: Arguing over the wording of school rules is forbidden.

27   Monday

28   Tuesday

29   Wednesday

30   Thursday

Friday

31

Saturday

Mothering Sunday **1**

Turnabout Day

Sunday

2

Octeday

FAMOUS INSTRUMENT OF DESPATCH:
Jewellery. Lady T'malia (BlackWidow).
Believed to have enough poison concealed
in the jewellery of one hand alone to poison
a continent. Very few shake hands with her
and live to boast of it.

3   Monday

4   Tuesday
●

5   Wednesday

6   Thursday

Friday
7

Saturday
8

Sunday
9

Octeday

GUILD COMMISSION: 'Bogey Bob', one of Ankh-Morpork's vagrant community, was killed by having a table nailed to his head by an unknown Assassin, who nevertheless left a receipt with an indecipherable signature. An appalling example of poor gamesmanship, and almost certain not to be the work of a real Guild member.

10 Monday

11 Tuesday

12 Wednesday

13 Thursday

Friday

14

Saturday

15

Sunday

16

Octeday

FAMOUS OLD BOY: Zlorf Flannelfoot (C1). Past President of the Guild. Mr Flannelfoot is the only Assassin in recent years to have risen to high office from low birth. Not a fast thinker in academic matters, he did have a good grasp of the principle of 'dead men's shoes'. Very badly scarred, giving people the impression that someone has been trying to cross out his face.

17

Monday

18

Tuesday

○

19

Wednesday

20

Thursday

Friday

Good Friday
Holiday in UK **21**

Saturday

22

Sunday

Easter Sunday
St George's Day **23**

Octeday

FAMOUS INSTRUMENT OF DESPATCH: Poisoned Sweets.
All students are warned against accepting sweets from
strangers or from Lord Downey (Mrs Beddowe's).

24 Easter Monday
Holiday in UK and
Republic of Ireland
Monday

25 Anzac Day
Tuesday

26
Wednesday

27
Thursday

Friday

Creator's Birthday

28

Saturday

29

Sunday

Beltane **30**

Octeday

MEMBER OF STAFF: The Extremely Rev. Dr A-Pox-Upon-Their-Houses Jenkins (Religious Studies). Although of the Omnian persuasion, the Rev. Jenkins is a practitioner of many other religions and says he is quite happy to believe anything. A speciality subject of his is hand-to-hand Smiting – not just hip and thigh, but at many little-known bones and muscles.

1 Holiday in UK and
Republic of Ireland

Monday

May Blossom Day

2

Tuesday

3

Wednesday

4 Labour Day
(Queensland)
●

Thursday

Friday

5

Saturday

6

Sunday

7

Octeday

GUILD COMMISSION: Olerve the Bastard, King of Sto Lat. Cleanly, with a crossbow, by Guillaume Dire (Pernypopax Dampier). Regrettably, this Old Boy was found poisoned two days after this commission was completed. It is believed that he was himself inhumed by his employer. This is always a possibility, and student Assassins are warned against accepting gifts of food or hospitality before the fee has been banked.

8   Monday

9   Tuesday

10   Wednesday

11   Thursday

Friday 12

Saturday 13

Sunday

Mother's Day (Australia,
New Zealand, Canada) 14

Octeday

FAMOUS INSTRUMENT OF DESPATCH:
A common teaspoon, wielded by the
Hon. Stanley Cabshaw against a group
of bandits on the Quirm road (a government
contract). Details are sketchy, and perhaps
this is just as well.

15
Monday

16
Tuesday

17
Wednesday

18
○
Thursday

Friday

19

Saturday

20

Sunday

21

Octeday

School Rule No. 150: Matters of a Delicate and/or Personal Nature may be discussed with Matron after tea on Tuesdays and Thursdays. Pupils must put their names on the list in Big School. Time-wasting with frivolous or irrelevant questions is punishable, as are anatomical questions of any description.

22 Monday

23 Tuesday

24 Wednesday

25 Thursday

Friday

26

Saturday

27

Sunday

28

Octeday

OPEN COMMISSION: Cmdr Vimes (AM$600,000, and rising). Cmdr Vimes rather irritatingly takes it all in good part. Many attempts have been made and the Assassins have, in the main, returned in one piece (albeit slightly singed, or painted yellow, or limping). Cmdr Vimes does not play by the rules – *any* rules.

29 Bank Holiday
in UK   **Monday**

30   **Tuesday**

31   **Wednesday**

1   **Thursday**

Friday

2
●

Saturday

3

Sunday

4

Octeday

DISGRACED OLD BOY: Stren Withel (Mrs Beddowe's). Mr Withel was expelled from the school when he was found by his Tutors to be enjoying himself too much. Worse than that, he was encouraging other boys to rowdy behaviour and mass turbulence, which has never been tolerated at the Guild.

5 Holiday in Republic
of Ireland

Monday

6

Tuesday

7

Wednesday

8

Thursday

Friday
9

On this day in 1901 William
Venturi, then Head Boy,
became the first person to
complete the new Assassin
Test by assassinating the tester.
This earned him maximum
marks, but the test procedure
was thereafter revised.

Saturday
10

Sunday
11

Octeday

MEMBER OF STAFF: Baron Strifenkanen
(Applied Pathology). The Baron is very much
a 'character' of the Guild, and the pupils
certainly enjoy his amusing practical jokes
and demonstrations of ventriloquism . . .

12   Monday

13   Tuesday

14   Wednesday

15   Thursday

Friday

16

○

Saturday

17

Sunday

Small Gods' Eve

Father's Day
(UK, Republic of
Ireland, Canada **18**

Octeday

Small Gods' Day

School Rule No.151: Lurking Behind The Stables: pupils not found lurking behind the stables at least once per term will be reprimanded; lurking is an essential skill and should be practised whenever possible. Pupils who can provide evidence that they were *in fact* lurking but were not spotted will be awarded a gold star on their report.

19 Monday

20 Tuesday

21 Wednesday
Longest day of the year
Litha (Summer Solstice)

22 Thursday

Friday

23

Saturday

24

Sunday

25

Octeday

FAMOUS OLD BOY: Pteppicymon XXXXX (Viper). Son of the Pharaoh of Djelibeybi, Pteppic passed with flying colours. His current whereabouts are unknown.

26   **Monday**

27   **Tuesday**

28   **Wednesday**

29   **Thursday**

Friday

Field Day

30

Saturday

Canada Day
Partial eclipse
of the sun

1
●

Sunday

2

Octeday

School Rule No. 152: Boys are not allowed to slide
down the coke heaps.

3

Monday

4

Tuesday

5

Wednesday

6

Thursday

Patrician's Day

Friday

7

Saturday

8

Sunday

9

Octeday

OPEN COMMISSION: Havelock, Lord Vetinari (AM$1m). Lord Vetinari is himself a graduate of the Guild and as such is a formidable opponent. Whilst he is known to view assassination attempts as a normal part of his life as a politician, and whilst he fully understands that the Guild's members are obliged to take on such commissions, he nevertheless takes a firm view that a dog only gets one bite. Most of the Assassins who have tried to earn the AM$1,000,000 fee have never been heard of since.

10 Monday

11 Tuesday

12 Holiday in Northern Ireland Wednesday

13 Thursday

Friday 14

Saturday 15

Sunday

Total eclipse of the moon 1303–1449

16

○

Octeday

FAMOUS INSTRUMENT OF DESPATCH: Mole. Sir Guy de Taupinier (Viper) had been commissioned to assassinate King Guillaume le Rouge. Seizing an opportunity during a deer hunt in the Royal Forest, Sir Guy used a catapult to propel a dead mole (found along the wayside) at the King, which knocked him from his horse, causing him to break his neck and die.

17 Monday

18 Tuesday

19 Wednesday

20 Thursday

Friday 21

Saturday 22

Sunday 23

Octeday

DISGRACED OLD BOY: Edward D'Eath (Viper). Not only did Edward kill without a valid commission but also, and more importantly, he stole Guild property. Unforgivable.

24   Monday

25   Tuesday

26   Wednesday

27   Thursday

Friday

de Murforte Day

28

Saturday

29

Sunday

30

Octeday

GUILD COMMISSION: Julian I, Emperor of Tsort. One of a thankfully few mass assassinations. Several Members had separately decided to go for the fairly large purse being offered by the then Empress of Tsort. In the event his bedroom was invaded at dead of night by Messrs Cascara (Scorpion), Cassawary (Mrs Beddowe's), Parmensis (Pernypopax Dampier) and Quintas (Viper), who each took an independent route and all, in the darkness, mistook one another for guards. Apparently the Emperor slept through the whole thing. This was an embarrassment to the Guild and the system was changed to avoid recurrences.

31 Partial eclipse
of the sun
●

Monday

1

Tuesday

2 Lammas
(Lughnasadh)

Wednesday

3

Thursday

Friday 4

Saturday 5

Sunday 6

Octeday

MEMBER OF STAFF: Mr Graumunchen ('You can't kill 'em, boyo, if you can't find 'em!') considers applied Geography to be a vital Assassin skill, and even runs special courses on flint knapping and obsidian working so that no Guild member, however extreme his circumstances, need be short of an edge. He is extremely proud of being one of the first dwarfs born in Ankh-Morpork, prouder still that he has never been down a mine, and declares that he wouldn't think of hitting a rock with anything bigger than a small hammer.

7 Holiday in Scotland
and Republic of Ireland

Monday

8 **Tuesday**

9 **Wednesday**

10 **Thursday**

Friday 11

Saturday 12

Sunday 13

Octeday

FAMOUS INSTRUMENT OF DESPATCH: Wallpaper.
One of the Emperors of Brindisi was inhumed by
Dr de Colleuse (Viper). Dr de Colleuse had planned to
inhume him by using poisoned wallpaper in the state
bedroom. He was, however, discovered in the act and
with great initiative, clubbed the Emperor to death
with one of the rolls of paper.

14   **Monday**

15   **Tuesday**
○

16   **Wednesday**

17   **Thursday**

Friday

18

Saturday

19

Sunday

20

Octeday

DISGRACED OLD BOY: Grav Drac von Glocken, Dragon King of Arms (B2). He designed the Guild's coat of arms and was also responsible for its motto. His own escutcheon was irrevocably blotted, though, when he was implicated in the circumstances surrounding a number of unpaid-for deaths in the city. Current whereabouts uncertain.

21 Monday

22 Tuesday

23 Wednesday

24 Thursday

Friday 25

Saturday 26

Sunday 27
Founder's Day

Octeday

FAMOUS INSTRUMENT OF DESPATCH: Mackerel.
The Grand Vizier of El Sanlu (Wigblock Prior) stabbed
to death the Emir of El Kaound with a frozen mackerel at
a dried-up oasis in the middle of the Great Nef, the Discworld's
hottest and driest desert. The Grand Vizier then died of wounds
from a blow from, apparently, a live turbot. There are many aspects
of this fight which remain a mystery.

28 Bank Holiday in
England, Wales and
Northern Ireland
Monday

29
●
Tuesday

30
Wednesday

31
Thursday

Friday 1

Saturday 2

Sunday

Father's Day
(Australia, New Zealand) 3

Octeday

GUILD COMMISSION: Patricio, Despot of Quirm.
The Guild's largest client, at 43 stone. A team led by
senior Assassin Lord Robert Selachii (Scorpion) and
Mr Sendivoge (Welcome Soap) inhumed the Despot,
with a break for lunch.

4 Labour Day
(Canada)

Monday

5

Tuesday

6

Wednesday

7

Thursday

Friday 8

Saturday 9

Sunday 10

Octeday

DISGRACED OLD BOY: Dr Cruces (Tree Frog). Not only did Dr Cruces fail dismally to complete the open commission on Lord Vetinari, but he also murdered an Old Sicarian and a member of the City Watch (that is to say, he killed without payment). *Not* a good example to younger Assassins.

11 Monday

12 Tuesday

13 Wednesday
○

14 Thursday

Friday

Olympic Games begin **15**

Saturday

16

Sunday

17

Octeday

School Rule No.167: Whilst the Guild encourages improving hobbies of all kinds, the following pursuits are banned on Guild premises: 1) Taxidermy of animals over 6" long; 2) Tanning; 3) the Training of wild animals (with the exception of white mice and the Brindisian Yodelling Stick-insect).

18   Monday

19   Tuesday

20   Wednesday

21   Thursday

Friday

Mabon
(Autumn Equinox) **22**

Saturday

23

Sunday

24

Octeday

OPEN COMMISSION: Corporal 'Nobby' Nobbs
(AM$4.31). This one is believed to be a joke
perpetrated by Cpl Nobbs' Watch colleagues.
Cmdr Vimes has let it be known that he would be
'upset' if this commission were to be carried out.

25 Monday

26 Tuesday

27 Wednesday
●

28 Thursday

Friday   29

Saturday   30

Sunday   Olympic Games end   1

Octeday

FAMOUS INSTRUMENT OF DESPATCH: A Butt of Brandy. On a
commission from the late Duke of Sto Helit, Mr R.P.W.Roberston
(Pernypopax Dampier) inhumed the Duke of Sto Kerrig by drowning
him in a barrel of best brandy. By a terrible accident, the sealed butt
was later bought by the Guild, and for some months members
commented upon the interesting smoky flavour. It was only when
the dye from the Duke's jacket turned the brandy green that the lid
was levered up and he was found, perfectly preserved and smiling . . .

2 Labour Day (ACT,
NSW, South Australia)   **Monday**

3   **Tuesday**

4   **Wednesday**

5   **Thursday**

Friday

6

Saturday

7

Sunday

8

Octeday

FAMOUS OLD BOY: '71-Hour' Ahmed
(Viper). Better known to Old Sicarians as
Ahmed the Bed-Wetter. Ahmed is now
the head of the Klatchian Police, reporting
direct to Prince Khufurah. Although Ahmed
does technically spend much of his time
killing people for money, he no longer
undertakes Guild commissions as such.

SEKTOBER / OCTOBER 2000

9 Thanksgiving
(Canada)

Monday

10

Tuesday

Soul Cake Day
(Soul Cake Tuesday)
Pullis Corvorum

11

Wednesday

Soul Cake Day

12

Thursday

Soul Cake Day

Friday 13

○

Saturday 14

Sunday 15

Octeday

School Rule No.169: No boy is allowed to grow a moustache until he is in the Sixth Form.

School Rule No.169a: In deference to the new arrangements, no girl is to grow a moustache until she is in the Sixth Form, either.

16   Monday

17   Tuesday

18   Wednesday

19   Thursday

General Inspection

Friday 20

Saturday 21

Sunday 22

Octeday

MEMBER OF STAFF: Miss Alice Band (Climbing, Traps, Locks, also private tuition in Stealth Archaeology, Pistol Bow, Croquet and Pianoforte). Miss Band has had a distinguished career at the more robust end of education, and her introduction of Free-Form Hockey to the Quirm College for Young Ladies is unlikely to be forgotten. Any senior pupils wishing to take (as she puts it) 'liberties' will be taught a lesson they will remember for the rest of their lives; they will not need long memories.

23 Labour Day
(New Zealand)   **Monday**

24   **Tuesday**

25   **Wednesday**

26   **Thursday**

Friday

27
●

Saturday

28

Sunday

British Summer
Time ends

29

Octeday

GUILD COMMISSION: Count Dragoul von Salic, of Uberwald. The Count was successfully inhumed by four separate generations of the same family – J.C.R. Wiggs, his son P.M.T. Wiggs, his grandson S.T.D. Wiggs and his great-grandson B.S.E. Wiggs (all of Viper). The Count is currently back on the Open Commissions List, and by general agreement will remain so until Miss Jocasta Wiggs graduates from the Guild.

30 Holiday in
Republic of Ireland

Monday

31 Samhain

Tuesday

1

Wednesday

2

Thursday

Friday 3

Saturday 4

Sunday 5

Octeday

FAMOUS INSTRUMENT OF DESPATCH: Exploding Privy. This was used by Mr Trefor Frame against Mr Edwin Cardly at a coaching inn in Slake. It was a matter of opportunity, a more elaborate death having been planned further along the road, but Mr Frame said 'It suddenly dawned on me that all I need do was throw my lighted cigar with extreme accuracy.'

6   **Monday**

7 Melbourne Cup Day (Victoria)   **Tuesday**

8   **Wednesday**

9   **Thursday**

Friday

10

Saturday

11
○

Sunday

Remembrance
Sunday (UK)

12

Octeday

FAMOUS OLD BOY: Charles H. J. Wiggs (Wigblock
Prior) of the famous Guild family never actually worked
as an Assassin, having been blown from the roof of the
Guild whilst returning to his study after taking his final
examination in hurricane conditions. He was awarded
an honorary pass and his parting was commemorated
by his father by the commissioning of the weather
vane which even now adorns the Guild.

13 Remembrance
Day (Canada)

Monday

14

Tuesday

15

Wednesday

On this day in 1832 the
practice of Slibbering was
forbidden in the school.

16

Thursday

Friday

17

Saturday

18

Sunday

19

Octeday

OPEN COMMISSION: The Duck Man (AM$132K). Despite the large reward, no Assassin has yet attempted this one. Everyone is too intrigued by this bizarre commission. The identity of the person behind this offer has never been revealed.

20   Monday

21   Tuesday

22   Wednesday

23   Thursday

Friday 24

Saturday 25
●

Sunday 26

Octeday

GUILD COMMISSION: Kang, Lord of Agatea. Swiftly, with a jigsaw puzzle, by H.K.Smarter (Viper). This one remains a mystery as Mr Smarter took the methodology with him to his grave.

27 Monday

28 Tuesday

29 Wednesday

30 St Andrew's Day Thursday

Friday

1

Saturday

2

Sunday

3

Octeday

FAMOUS INSTRUMENT OF DESPATCH: Sledgehammer.
F.D.R. Mason (Mykkim) was the first Assassin to undertake a
commission against a troll, attempting to despatch Mr Marble
by hitting him over the head with a sledgehammer outside an
inn in the Shades. Mr Mason's eventual return to the Guild
was slightly marred by his being pushed under the main door.
Students returning from an evening's drinking mistook him for
an ornamental doormat and his fate was not discovered until morning.

4   Monday

5   Tuesday

6   Wednesday

7   Thursday

Friday 8

Saturday 9

Sunday 10

Octeday

School Rule No.170: No pupil is to try to walk like Mr Lamister.

11 Monday

○

12 Tuesday

13 Wednesday

14 Thursday

Friday

15

Carol Service: Eight
Lessons and Carols
for Hogswatch

Saturday

16

Sunday

17

Octeday

DISGRACED OLD BOY: Mr Teatime (B2). Mr Teatime
failed to carry out a major commission for which the
Guild had been paid a very large sum of money indeed.
Also, his essay, 'Who I Killed on My Holidays', is
considered to be a pathetic flight of juvenile imagination
copied from a work of fiction in the Guild library, *Decem
Parvi Indi.*

18   Monday

19   Tuesday

20   Wednesday

21   Shortest day of the year   Thursday
Yule (Winter Solstice)

Friday

22

Saturday

23

Sunday

Christmas Eve **24**

Octeday

25 Christmas Day
Partial eclipse of
the sun
● **Monday**

26 Boxing Day
St Stephen's Day **Tuesday**

27 **Wednesday**

28 **Thursday**

Friday 29

Saturday 30
Hogswatch Eve

Sunday New Year's Eve 31
Hogswatchnight

Octeday ICK

NOTES

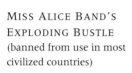

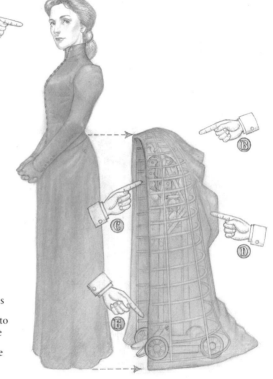

MISS ALICE BAND'S
EXPLODING BUSTLE
(banned from use in most
civilized countries)

KEY

A Miss Band

B Bustle on wicker frame; space
below easily accommodates
additional weaponry in case of
Eventualities

C 'Falchion' Compressed Air
Device, lethal in a ten-yard radius

D Adjustable Timer Mechanism to
allow swift yet ladylike departure

E Hidden pedal-operated Release
Mechanism and Primer

First published in Great Britain 1999 by Victor Gollancz Ltd
An imprint of Orion Books Ltd, Orion House, 5 Upper St Martin's Lane, London WC2H 9EA
Text © 1999 Terry and Lyn Pratchett, and Stephen Briggs
Illustrations © 1999 Paul and Sandra Kidby
Discworld® is a trade mark registered by Terry Pratchett.
All rights reserved.
The right of Terry Pratchett and Stephen Briggs to be identified as authors of this work
has been asserted by them under the Copyright, Designs and Patents Act, 1988.
ISBN 0 575 06687 3
Printed in Great Britain by Butler & Tanner Ltd, London and Frome
To receive information on the Gollancz/Millennium list, e-mail us at: smy@orionbooks.co.uk

The publishers have taken every care in the preparation of the information contained
in this diary but cannot be held responsible for the consequences of any inaccuracies.

DISCWORLD® MERCHANDISE direct from C. M. O. T. Dibbler
An exclusive range of badges, T-shirts, scarves – including the new Assassins' Guild Prefect badge – is
available from Stephen Briggs. Also, you can graduate from UU. Full details from sbriggs@cix.co.uk or
s.a.e. to Stephen Briggs, PO Box 655, Oxford OX4 3EU.

YEAR PLANNER 2001

	January	February	March	April	May	June
Mon	1					
Tues	2				1	
Wed	3				2	
Thu	4	1	1		3	
Fri	5	2	2		4	1
Sat	6	3	3		5	2
Sun	7	4	4	1	6	3
Mon	8	5	5	2	7	4
Tues	9	6	6	3	8	5
Wed	10	7	7	4	9	6
Thu	11	8	8	5	10	7
Fri	12	9	9	6	11	8
Sat	13	10	10	7	12	9
Sun	14	11	11	8	13	10
Mon	15	12	12	9	14	11
Tues	16	13	13	10	15	12
Wed	17	14	14	11	16	13
Thu	18	15	15	12	17	14
Fri	19	16	16	13	18	15
Sat	20	17	17	14	19	16
Sun	21	18	18	15	20	17
Mon	22	19	19	16	21	18
Tues	23	20	20	17	22	19
Wed	24	21	21	18	23	20
Thu	25	22	22	19	24	21
Fri	26	23	23	20	25	22
Sat	27	24	24	21	26	23
Sun	28	25	25	22	27	24
Mon	29	26	26	23	28	25
Tues	30	27	27	24	29	26
Wed	31	28	28	25	30	27
Thu			29	26	31	28
Fri			30	27		29
Sat			31	28		30
Sun				29		
Mon				30		
Tues						

Offle	February	March	April	May	June